**Vocal Selections from the Motion P**

Applications for performance of this work, whether legitimate, stock, amateur, or foreign, should be addressed to:
JOSEF WEINBERGER LTD.
12-14 MORTIMER STREET
LONDON W1N 7RD

# Annie

# MAYBE

Lyric by MARTIN CHARNIN
Music by CHARLES STROUSE

# TOMORROW

Lyric by Martin Charnin
Music by Charles Strouse

# IT'S THE HARD-KNOCK LIFE

Lyric by Martin Charnin
Music by Charles Strouse

14

Annie ™

# WE GOT ANNIE

Lyric by Martin Charnin
Music by Charles Strouse

She's like a shine on your shoes_ or hear-in' a blues_ that's great_

Makes you re - lax_ like a big tax_ re - bate.

*Spoken:* We Got An-nie!

We Got An - nie, We Got

Spoken: We Got An-nie!

# I THINK I'M GONNA LIKE IT HERE

Lyric by Martin Charnin
Music by Charles Strouse

# SANDY
## (Dumb Dog)

Lyric by Martin Charnin
Music by Charles Strouse

# LET'S GO TO THE MOVIES

Lyric by Martin Charnin
Music by Charles Strouse

# SIGN!

Lyric by Martin Charnin
Music by Charles Strouse

# I DON'T NEED ANYTHING BUT YOU

Lyric by Martin Charnin
Music by Charles Strouse

# YOU'RE NEVER FULLY DRESSED
# WITHOUT A SMILE

Lyric by Martin Charnin
Music by Charles Strouse

# LITTLE GIRLS

Lyric by Martin Charnin
Music by Charles Strouse

# EASY STREET

Lyric by Martin Charnin
Music by Charles Strouse

Annie™

# Annie